Bottle Boggle

You slip into Egypt by crossing the Mediterranean Sea. As you glide into the port city of Alexandria, you think about the adventure ahead. Suddenly you spot a Top Secret bottle floating by with a message in it!

To crack the code, first check the Top Secret Tip. Then follow the message directions carefully. They will provide your first important clue.

1. Write the name of your boat on this line.

2. Cross out **CL**. In their place put **MD** and write the string of letters again.

3. Find the place where two vowels are next to each other. Put an **N** between them and write the letters again.

4. Cross out the third and fifth letters and write the rest of the letters on this line.

5. Replace the letters **TR** with **WS**.

6. Add an **A** somewhere in the string of letters to make a three-letter word meaning "angry."

7. Cross out the letter that is 16th in the alphabet.

8. Turn the word around by writing the letters from last to first.

Your boat is named the CLEOPATRA.

TOP SECRET TIP

Write the letters from Step 8 on the dashes below. The stolen object is not hidden at the

__ __ __ __ __ __ __ __ __ __ .

Turn to page 30 in this puzzle book and cross off the one place where the stolen item is not hidden.

Answer on page 32.

Use your villain cards to help you locate the crooks. They are wearing the same clothes as on the cards.

TOP SECRET TIP

HIDDEN CROOKS

From Alexandria, you travel east to Cairo, Egypt's largest city. After changing your clothes, you stroll out into the streets. Your first stop is the Mosque of Al-Azhar, the oldest university in the city. You join students, teachers, and pilgrims who visit this Muslim shrine.

Beware, Top Secret Agent! Five of the suspects are in the crowd, too. The sixth one was carried away in a *khamasin,* or dust storm, and picked up by the local police.

When you have found five suspects, turn to page 28. Cross off the thief you did not find. That villain could not have committed the crime.

Answer on page 32.

BIZARRE BAZAAR

Your next stop is the famous bazaar at Khan al-Khalili. While shopping for information, you discover a great deal. One of the merchants has a clue for you. But which one?

To find the clue, read what each person is saying. Only one statement is true. After you find the true fact, check the box on the next page.

You will need your Top Secret Guidebook for this one. The page number near each merchant will help you find the one true answer.

Jigsaw Treasure

To solve this case, you will need to know a lot about this country's past. So before leaving Cairo you head to the Egyptian Museum. You find a collection of ancient Egyptian treasures. Two rooms are filled with the golden treasures of King Tutankhamen. The greatest treasure of all is the clue waiting for you. To figure it out, find the one jigsaw piece that correctly completes the picture. Then check the box below.

BROOCH

EARRING

NECKLACE

BRACELET

All of the puzzle pieces are the correct shape. You need to find the one that completes the picture.

TOP SECRET TIP

Did you find the one piece that fits the puzzle? Now turn to page 29. Write the word next to that piece on line 2.

Answer on page 32.

Pyramid Power

Like most visitors to Egypt, you decide to see the pyramids. It's easy to see how the Great Pyramid at Giza got its name. It's huge! If you use a little math to figure out just how big the Great Pyramid is, you'll find your next clue.

Use the statements below to figure out the weight of the pyramid. Then, find the weight of each set of objects on the next page. Use the one that exactly matches the weight of the pyramid to discover your next clue.

- Each block of limestone weighs 5,000 pounds.
- There are 2,300,000 blocks of limestone in the Great Pyramid.
- How many pounds does the Great Pyramid weigh?

  $5,000 \times 2,300,000 =$

  a. 11,500,000 pounds
  b. 115,000,000 pounds
  c. 11,500,000,000 pounds

You have to multiply to figure out these clues. You may need a calculator to find the answers.

TOP SECRET TIP

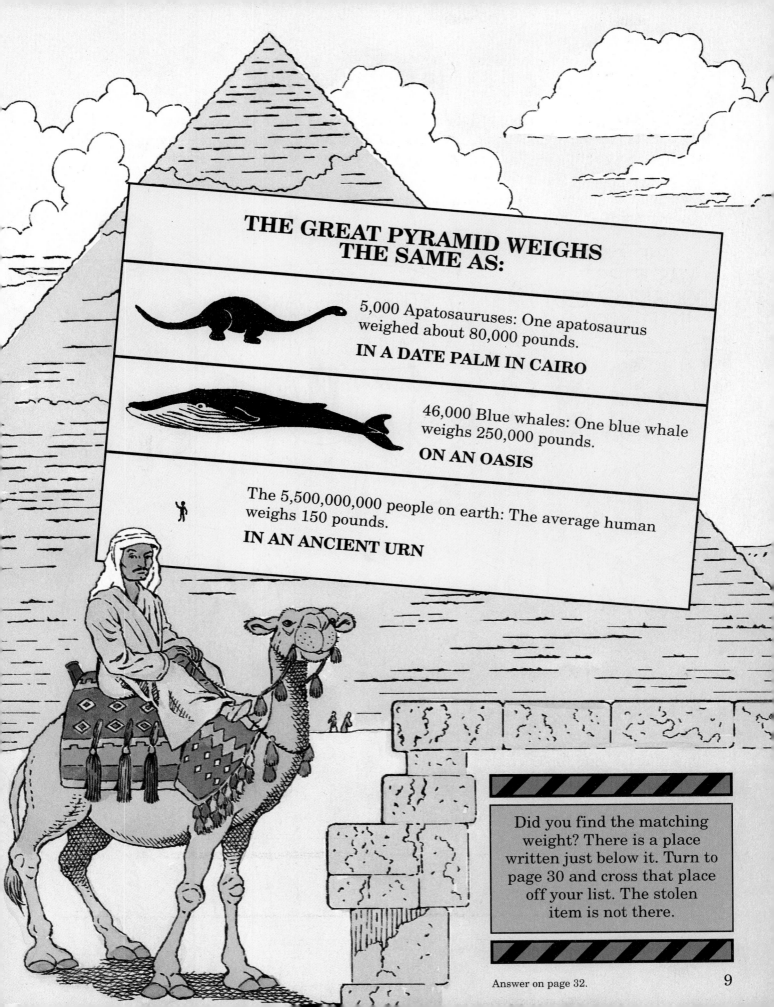

THE GREAT PYRAMID WEIGHS THE SAME AS:

5,000 Apatosauruses: One apatosaurus weighed about 80,000 pounds.

IN A DATE PALM IN CAIRO

46,000 Blue whales: One blue whale weighs 250,000 pounds.

ON AN OASIS

The 5,500,000,000 people on earth: The average human weighs 150 pounds.

IN AN ANCIENT URN

Did you find the matching weight? There is a place written just below it. Turn to page 30 and cross that place off your list. The stolen item is not there.

Answer on page 32.

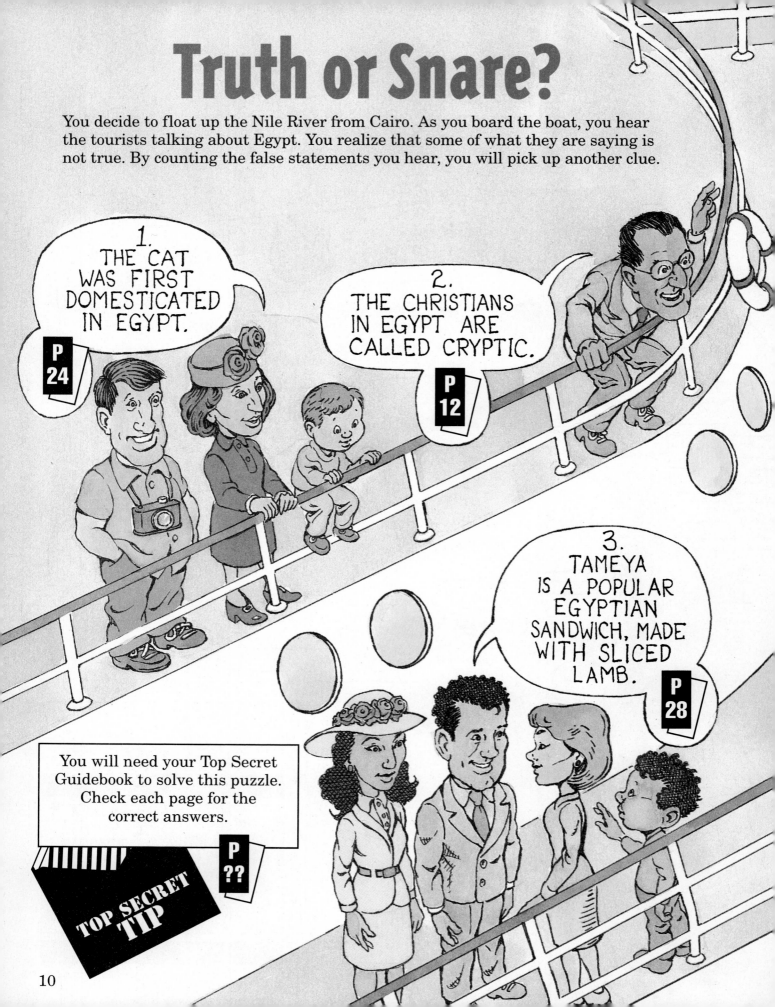

Truth or Snare?

You decide to float up the Nile River from Cairo. As you board the boat, you hear the tourists talking about Egypt. You realize that some of what they are saying is not true. By counting the false statements you hear, you will pick up another clue.

Count the number of statements that were false. Find the matching numbers below. Then turn to page 30. Cross off the place where the stolen item is not hidden.

If one was false, cross off *between the feet of the Sphinx.*
If two were false, cross off *the date palm in Cairo.*
If three were false, cross off *the pigeon palace.*

Answer on page 32.

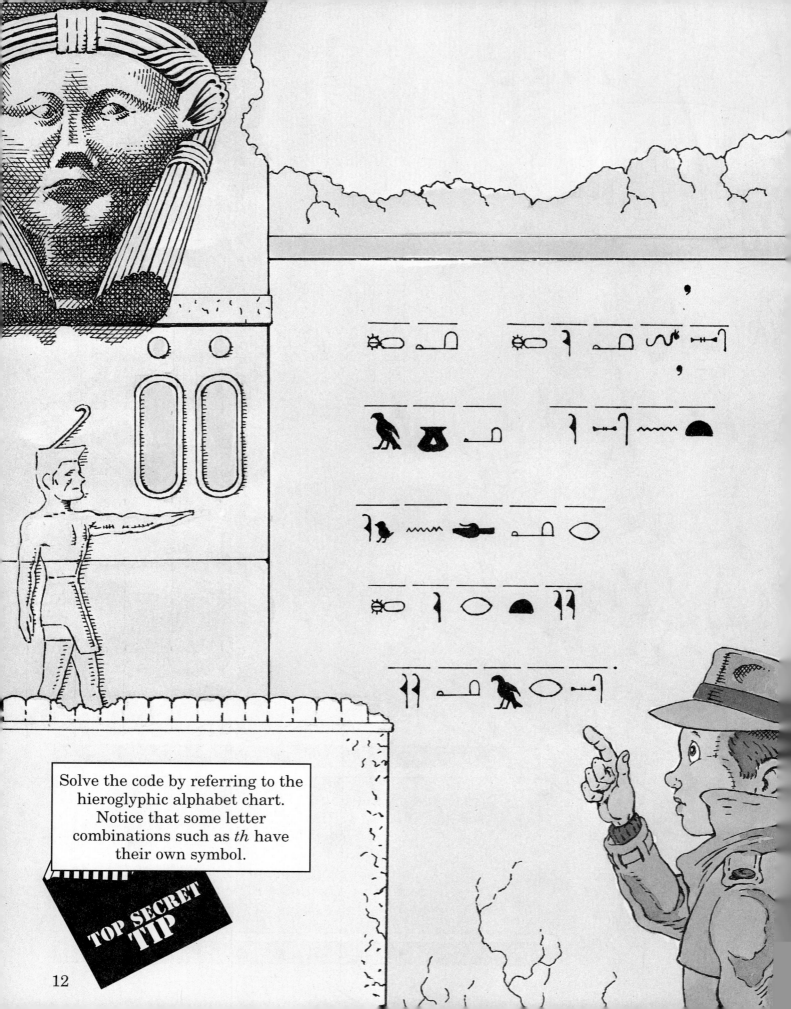

Solve the code by referring to the hieroglyphic alphabet chart. Notice that some letter combinations such as *th* have their own symbol.

TOP SECRET TIP

HIEROGLYPHS	LETTERS
	A
	B
	CH
	D
	E
	F
	G
	I
	J
	K
	M
	N
	P
	Q
	R
	S
	SH
	T
	TH
	U
	W
	Y

HIEROGLYPHIC CODE

As the boat chugs up the Nile, it stops so passengers can explore pyramids and temples. Many of the walls and columns are covered with *hieroglyphics*. These symbols were used for reading and writing in ancient Egypt.

While studying the hieroglyphics on one wall, you realize that you've stumbled upon a clue! Use the symbols to fill in the message on page 12.

Turn to page 28 and cross off the crook that couldn't have committed the crime according to the hieroglyphic message.
Hint: Your villain cards will help.

Answer on page 32.

It's the Pits!

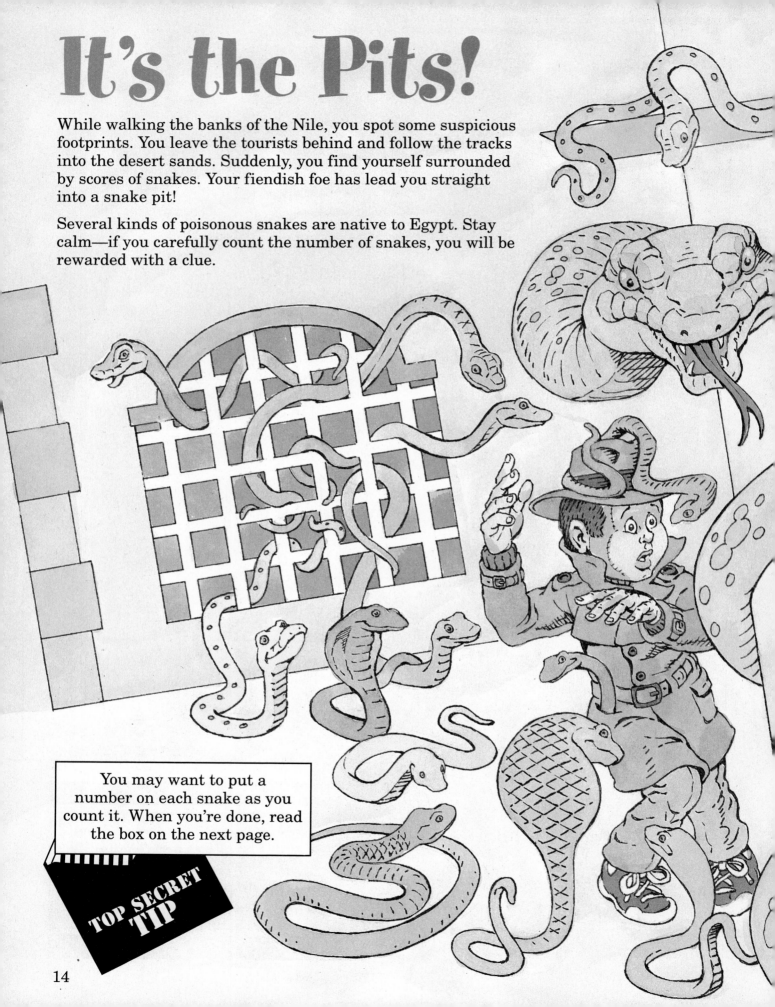

While walking the banks of the Nile, you spot some suspicious footprints. You leave the tourists behind and follow the tracks into the desert sands. Suddenly, you find yourself surrounded by scores of snakes. Your fiendish foe has lead you straight into a snake pit!

Several kinds of poisonous snakes are native to Egypt. Stay calm—if you carefully count the number of snakes, you will be rewarded with a clue.

You may want to put a number on each snake as you count it. When you're done, read the box on the next page.

TOP SECRET TIP

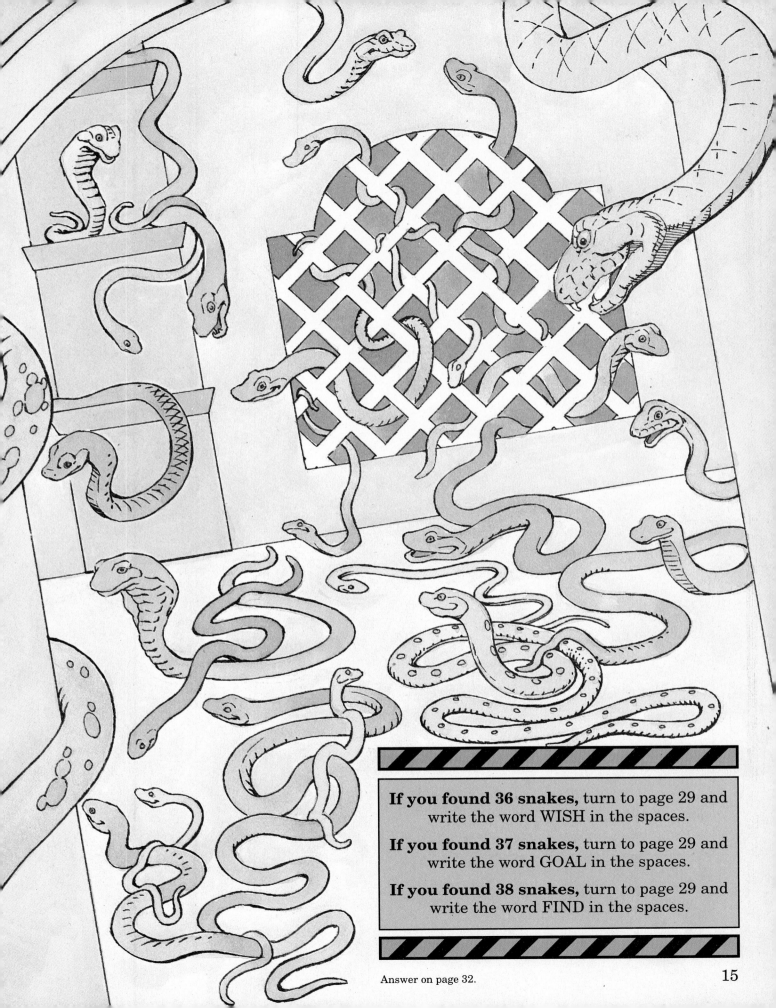

If you found 36 snakes, turn to page 29 and write the word WISH in the spaces.

If you found 37 snakes, turn to page 29 and write the word GOAL in the spaces.

If you found 38 snakes, turn to page 29 and write the word FIND in the spaces.

Answer on page 32.

Nomad KNOW-HOW

You escape unharmed from the snake pit, but you're still in trouble. It's getting dark, and you're alone in the middle of the desert. You spot a group of figures moving nearby. That's no mirage, Top Secret Agent! It's a group of desert people called *bedouins*. They will help you get safely through the night and provide you with another clue.

All the nomads think they saw the thief, but only one of them really did. To find the nomad who can help you, check the clues on page 17.

Read the clues in the box carefully. Use them to cross off each bedouin who does not have the correct information.

TOP SECRET TIP

NO. THE THIEF WAS NOT WEARING A BOW TIE.

THE THIEF WAS DEFINITELY A MAN.

I SAW SOMEONE WEARING A BOW TIE.

LAILA HUSSEIN ABDALLA JAMILA OMAR ANWAR

CLUES

1. The nomad who saw the crook does not have a beard.
2. Abdalla and Laila are married.
3. The nomad who saw the crook is single.
4. The nomad who saw the crook isn't a woman.

Did you figure out who has the correct information? Turn to page 28, and cross off any suspect who is the *opposite* of this clue.

GAME SHOW

With the help of your bedouin friends, you find the way back to the
tour boat. When you arrive, everyone is involved in a game. There's
a clue for you on the game board. Here's how to figure it out.

1. Place a penny
   or counter on
   START.

2. Answer the
   multiple choice
   question on the
   first card on the
   next page. Move
   your penny forward
   that number of
   spaces.

3. Answer the next
   question.
   Move forward that
   number of spaces.

4. When you have
   answered all the
   questions, the number in
   the space you are on is
   the key to your next clue.

You will need your Top Secret
Guidebook for this puzzle. The
guidebook symbol shows you
where to find each answer.

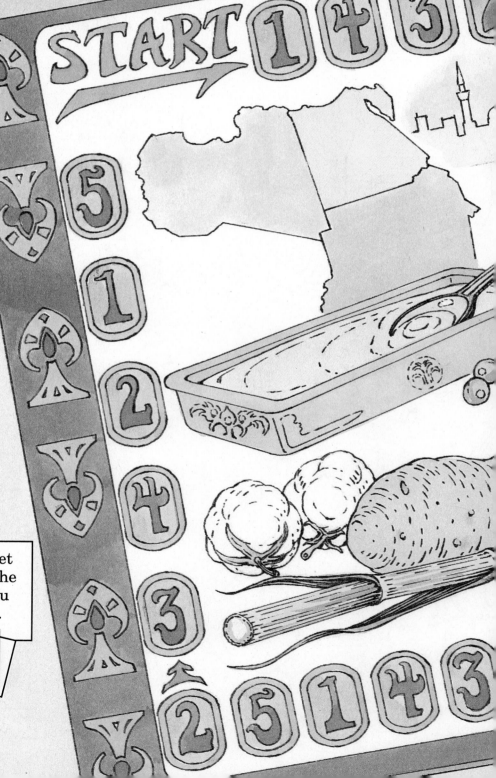

1. Egypt borders which two other African countries?
   a. Libya and Sudan *(Move 1 square.)*
   b. Morocco and Sudan *(Move 2 squares.)*
   c. Libya and Ethiopia *(Move 3 squares.)*

   P 5

2. The Suez canal ends at what city on the Mediterranean?
   a. Alexandria *(Move 2 squares.)*
   b. Suez *(Move 3 squares.)*
   c. Port Said *(Move 4 squares.)*

   P 24

3. What is the name of the paste-like food made from chick-peas?
   a. Tahini *(Move 5 squares.)*
   b. Hummus *(Move 3 squares.)*
   c. Ful medames *(Move 1 square.)*

   P 28

4. What name is used for the farmers who live in the Nile Valley?
   a. Fellahin *(Move 6 squares.)*
   b. Nubians *(Move 4 squares.)*
   c. Souks *(Move 2 squares.)*

   P 14

5. What is the most important crop in the Nile Valley?
   a. Sugarcane *(Move 2 squares.)*
   b. Cotton *(Move 1 square.)*
   c. Potatoes *(Move 3 squares.)*

   P 14

Turn to page 29. Write the number you landed on in the correct space.

Answer on page 32.

King-Sized Search

You are running out of leads in the present. Now it is time to look to the past for help. You have been learning a lot of names of the ancient rulers in Egypt. Some of these people lived more than five thousand years ago!

Find all of the names of the ancient kings in the word search. After you've circled all the names, the other letters will spell out an important message.

The names are hidden up, down, across, and diagonally. Some are written backward.

TOP SECRET TIP

WORD LIST

AMENEMHAT
AMENHOTEP
AMOSIS
APRIES
HATSHEPSUT
KHAFRE
KHUFU
MANKAURE
MENES
MERNEPTAH
NYUSERRE
RAMESSES
SENUSERT
SETI
SHABAKA
SHEPSESKAFE
TUTANKHAMUN
TUTHMOSIS
UNAS

```
H A T P E N R E M C R O
S K M T U T H M O S I S
S H O E F K F T H H T A
T U T A N K H A M U N M
R F A M E H B A S A S E
E U P N A A O P F I E N
S N R I K N E T S R N E
U A I A T H K O E C E M
N S E S S E M A R P M H
E I S T E A S N U T U A
S R A N Y U S E R R E T
S H E P S E S K A F E N
```

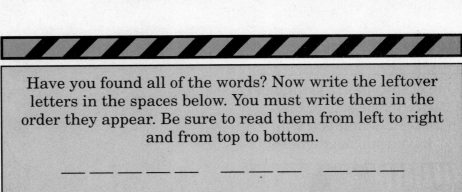

Have you found all of the words? Now write the leftover letters in the spaces below. You must write them in the order they appear. Be sure to read them from left to right and from top to bottom.

__ __ __ __ __ __ __   __ __   __ __ __

__ __ __ __ __ __ __   __ __ __

Now turn to page 30 and follow these instructions.

Answer on page 33.

Red Sea See

Your tour travels east to the Red Sea. You stop at the scientific station near Hurghada. Hot and tired after your journey, you grab your swim fins and dive into the water! As you snorkel through the water you discover more than fish.

Search this scene for the following items: a three-leafed clover, a compact disc, a jeweled purse, a hand mirror, a calculator, and one swim fin. When you have found them all, check the box on the next page.

One of the objects is hidden twice in the scene. Find that item and you will have your next clue.

TOP SECRET TIP

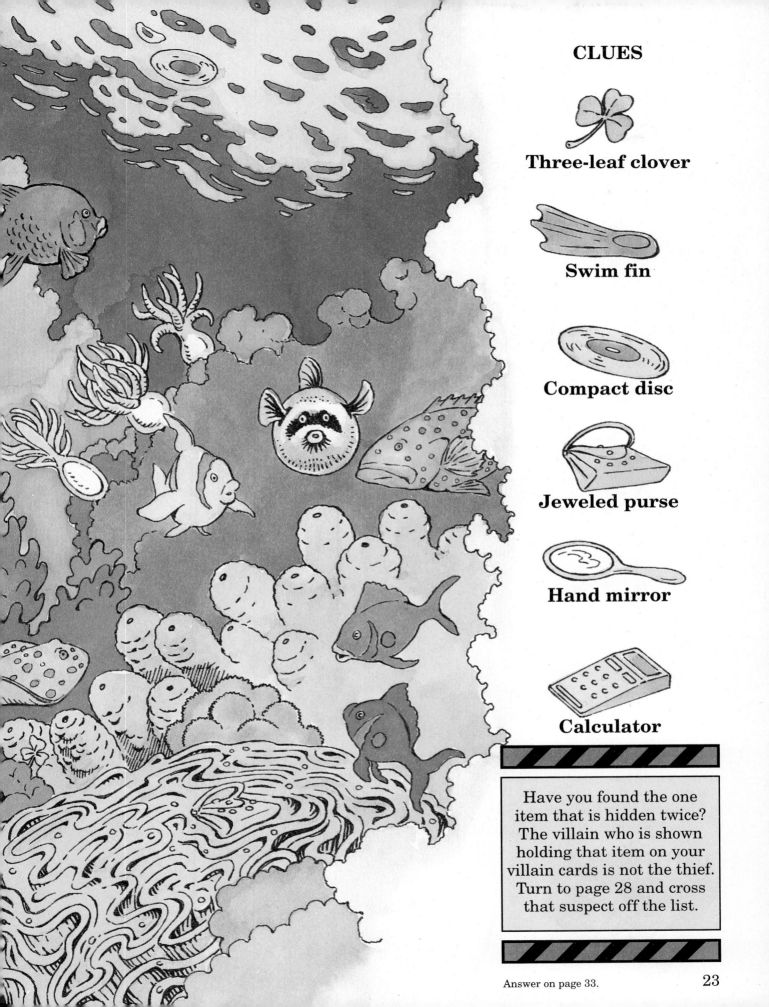

CLUES

Three-leaf clover

Swim fin

Compact disc

Jeweled purse

Hand mirror

Calculator

Have you found the one item that is hidden twice? The villain who is shown holding that item on your villain cards is not the thief. Turn to page 28 and cross that suspect off the list.

Answer on page 33.

OASIS

FINISH

START

SPHINX

FINISH

You can reach the inner chamber
of only one of the temples. When
you find the correct temple,
look at the box on page 25.

TOP SECRET TIP

24

TeMPLe TAngle

Once again heading south on the Nile, you reach the Valley of
Kings. Top Secret Headquarters has left a clue for you here.
It's in the tomb at the center of one of the ancient temples. To
find the correct one, follow the paths. Only one leads to the
center. When you find it, check the box below.

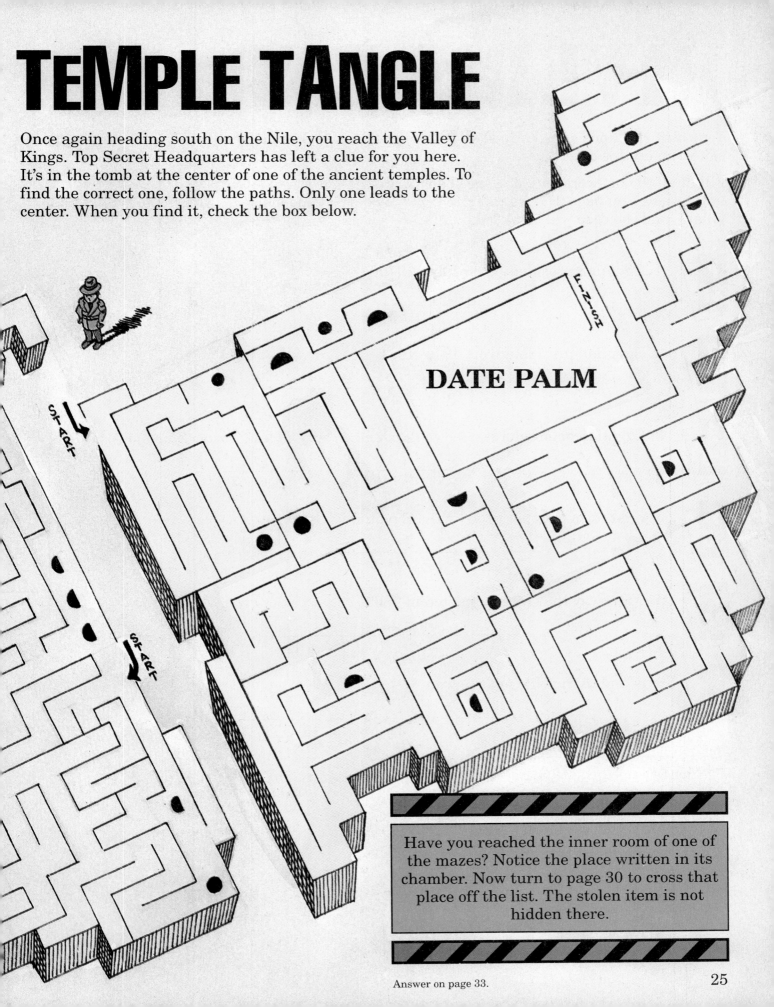

DATE PALM

START

START

FINISH

Have you reached the inner room of one of
the mazes? Notice the place written in its
chamber. Now turn to page 30 to cross that
place off the list. The stolen item is not
hidden there.

Answer on page 33.

RIVER'S END

Your boat ride ends at Lake Nasser. Solve one more puzzle, and you can wrap up this case.

Fill in all the answers for this page. Then write the numbered letters in the spaces on page 27. Use this final clue to cross off one more villain, and the case will be closed.

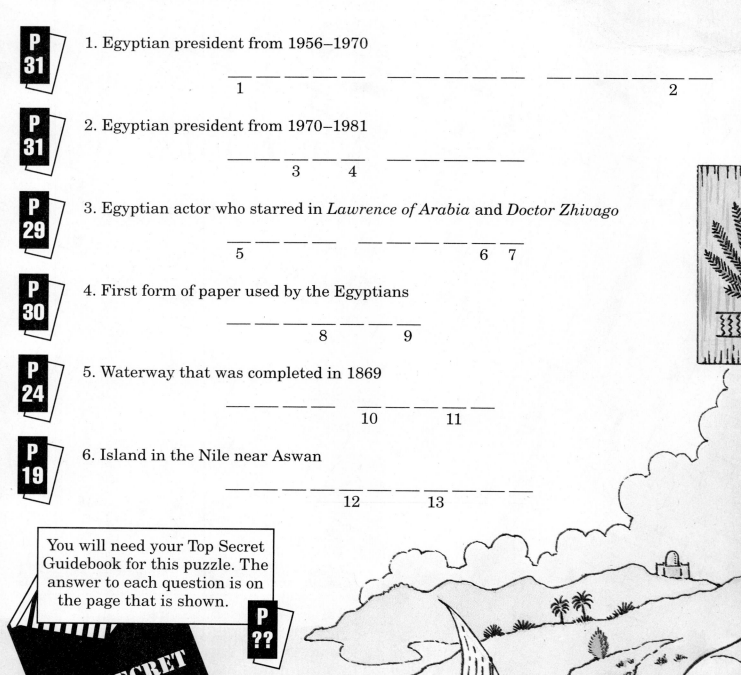

P 31 1. Egyptian president from 1956–1970

— — — — —   — — — — —   — — — — —
1   2

P 31 2. Egyptian president from 1970–1981

— — — — —   — — — — —
   3   4

P 29 3. Egyptian actor who starred in *Lawrence of Arabia* and *Doctor Zhivago*

— — — —   — — — — —
5   6   7

P 30 4. First form of paper used by the Egyptians

— — — — — — —
      8   9

P 24 5. Waterway that was completed in 1869

— — — —   — — — —
            10   11

P 19 6. Island in the Nile near Aswan

— — — — — — — —
         12   13

> You will need your Top Secret Guidebook for this puzzle. The answer to each question is on the page that is shown.
>
> **P ??**
>
> TOP SECRET TIP

$\overline{10}$ $\overline{4}$ $\overline{5}$ $\overline{9}$ $\overline{9}$ $\overline{5}$ $\overline{7}$ $\overline{7}$ $\overline{13}$ $\overline{12}$ $\overline{2}$ $\overline{13}$ $\overline{12}$ $\overline{6}$ $\overline{2}$ $\overline{7}$ $\overline{3}$ $\overline{6}$ $\overline{13}$ $\overline{12}$

$\overline{1}$ $\overline{4}$ $\overline{11}$ $\overline{8}$ $\overline{12}$ $\overline{11}$ $\overline{6}$ $\overline{4}$

Answer on page 33.

WHO DID IT?

To find the crook, you must solve the puzzles on pages 2, 12, 16, 22, and 26. Each time you solve a puzzle, you will be able to cross off one suspect from your list. When there's only one suspect left, you will have cracked the case!

SUSPECT LIST

Bjorn Luzer

Delta Nyle

Mimi Love

Sir Miser

The Mummy

Jewell Sparkle

When you cross off a suspect, do it in pencil. That way, if you solved a puzzle incorrectly, you can redo some steps. If your list gets too messy, try copying it onto another sheet of paper.

FINAL ANSWER:
The crook who did it is

TOP SECRET TIP

WHAT WAS STOLEN?

To find out what was stolen, you must solve the puzzles that begin on pages 4, 6, 14, and 18. One puzzle will give you the number of shapes you should color in the grid. Three puzzles will provide words to be written in the spaces below. When you have entered all of the words, you can transfer the letters to the spaces at the bottom of the page. After you have solved all of the puzzles, you will have discovered what was stolen.

Answer 1 (from page 5) ___ ___ ___ ___ ___
                          11 14 1   5   6

Answer 2 (from page 6) ___ ___ ___ ___ ___ ___ ___ ___
                          12 9   10 7   17 4   13 15

Answer 3 (from page 15) ___ ___ ___ ___
                          2   3   8   16

Color in the shapes that contain the number _____ (from page 19).

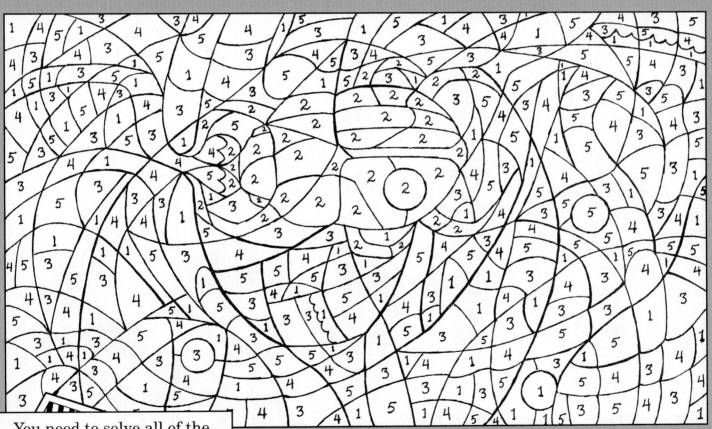

You need to solve all of the "What Was Stolen?" puzzles in order to make sense of the final solution.

TOP SECRET TIP

FINAL ANSWER:
The stolen item was

___ ___ ___ ___ ___ ___ ___ ___ ___ ___ ___
 1   2   3   4   5   6   7   8   9   10 11

___ ___ ___ ___ ___ ___ .
 12 13 14 15 16 17

WHERE IS IT HIDDEN?

The stolen item is hidden in one of the places listed below. To find out which one, you must solve the puzzles on pages 1, 8, 10, 20, and 24. Each time you solve a puzzle, you will eliminate one of the places from the list. In the end, you will be left with one location—that's the place where the loot is hidden.

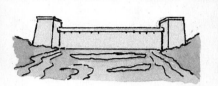

1. At the Aswan Dam

2. On an oasis

3. In a date palm in Cairo

4. Between the feet of the Sphinx

5. In an ancient urn

6. In a pigeon palace

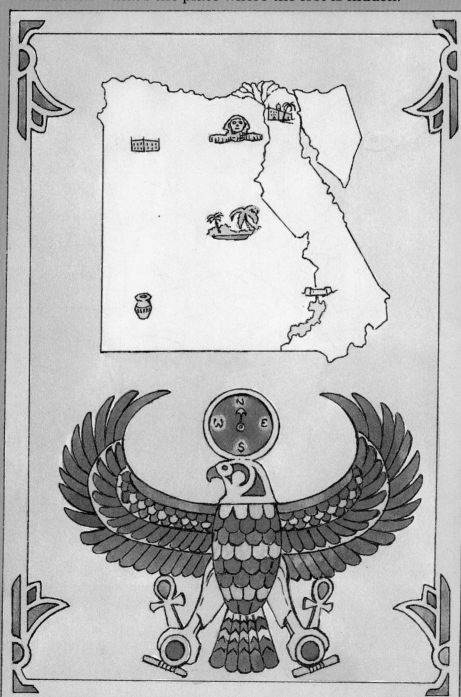

TOP SECRET DECODER PAGE

Use the extra space on this page to work out your puzzles.

The next two pages contain the answers for every puzzle and
for the Top Secret Mystery. Do not peek unless you're stuck on
a puzzle and need help.

TOP SECRET ANSWER KEY

Note: Many Egyptian words have more than one correct spelling. For example, *Ramesses* is often spelled *Ramses;* and *hummus, humus,* and *hommos* are all correct.

PAGE 1: BOTTLE BOGGLE
1. Cleopatra 2. Mdeopatra 3. Mdenopatra
4. Mdnpatra 5. Mdnpawsa 6. Madnpawsa
7. Madnawsa 8. Aswandam

The stolen object is not hidden at the ASWAN DAM. Cross it off on page 30.

PAGES 2-3: HIDDEN CROOKS
MIMI LOVE is not in the picture. Turn to page 28 and cross her off.

PAGES 4-5: BIZARRE BAZAAR

The bead seller ("Look in the desert ...") is making the true statement. Write BEADS in the spaces on page 29.

PAGES 6-7: JIGSAW MURAL

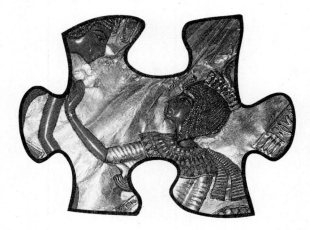

The piece next to the word BRACELET fits the puzzle. Write that word in the spaces on page 29.

PAGES 8-9: PYRAMID POWER
Cross off the OASIS on page 30. The Great Pyramid weighs 11,500,000,000 pounds, about the same as 46,000 blue whales. That huge number in words is: eleven billion, five hundred million.

PAGES 10-11: TRUTH OR SNARE?
Three statements are false (2, 3, and 4). Cross the PIGEON PALACE off the list on page 30.

PAGES 12-13: HIEROGLYPHIC CODE
"The thief's age isn't under thirty years" means that any suspect who *is* under 30 could not be the thief. Mimi Love and Delta Nyle are under 30, but Mimi was already eliminated. So cross off Delta on page 28.

PAGES 14-15: IT'S THE PITS!
There are 37 snakes. Write the word GOAL in the spaces on page 29.

PAGES 16-17: NOMAD KNOW-HOW

Hussein is the one who saw the real thief—someone *without* a bow tie. Cross off Bjorn Luzer, the only suspect *with* a bow tie.

PAGES 18-19: GAME SHOW
1. a—Libya and Sudan border Egypt.
2. c—The Suez Canal ends at Port Said.
3. b—Hummus is a paste-like food made from chick-peas.
4. a—Fellahin is the name used for farmers who live in the Nile Valley.
5. b—Cotton is the most important crop in the Nile Valley.

You will end on the number 2. Write it in the space on page 29 and then color in the shapes that contain a 2.